# Windigo and other tales of the Ojibways

*Windigo*

# Windigo

~and other tales of the Ojibways
Herbert  T.  Schwarz ~illustrated
by Norval Morrisseau MCCLELLAND
AND STEWART LIMITED, TORONTO/MONTREAL

© 1969 by Herbert T. Schwarz

*The Canadian Publishers*
McClelland and Stewart Limited
25 Hollinger Road, Toronto 16

Printed and bound in England
by Purnell & Sons Limited

*The Indians of Canada bid you welcome.*
*Walk in our moccasins the trail of our past.*
*Live with us in the here and now.*
*Talk with us by the fire of the days to come.*

THEME : CANADIAN INDIAN PAVILION, EXPO 67, MONTREAL.

 # Introduction

NORVAL MORRISSEAU: ARTIST
AND STORY-TELLER

This book was inspired by Norval Morrisseau, whose paintings and stories have filled our house on many an evening with mystery, awe and humour.

Norval Morrisseau, or Copper Thunderbird, as he is known among his people, is an Ojibway Indian who was born and raised in northern Ontario. The Ojibways, a great and proud nation, once ranged over the vast Lake Nipigon – Thunder Bay area extending north and west from Lake Superior. They were, however, an illiterate and primitive people, whose only literature was oral tradition and whose only art was that which adorned their garments. They proved little challenge for the white man, whose relentless progress eventually deprived them of their land and livelihood, and brought them in return smallpox, tuberculosis, whisky and prostitution. Not understanding the white man's ways, they defied science and the machine, and clung to the very ancient loyalties which they now saw defiled. Eroded and demoralized, they perished as a nation.

Then, among these wordless and defeated people, a man was born who had vivid visions of their past greatness, and the strength and insight to recognize the value of their legends. He broke the taboos and began to paint the ancient stories, thus saving them from passing into total oblivion.

This was Norval Morrisseau, a unique personality in the history of Canadian art. His formal education ended with grade three, and his health was impaired by starvation, personal excesses, heavy labour in the gold mines and the inevitable tuberculosis. Although he had had no instruction in art, Morrisseau became a compulsive painter, working incessantly on whatever materials were available – sheets of birch bark or plywood, scraps of paper or animal hide.

On the subject of his art, Morrisseau speaks thus:

*Among the Indians, as among other nations, some people are born artists, but most are not. I am a born artist. I have as much interest in my people as any anthropologist, and I have studied our culture and lore. My aim is to reassemble the pieces of a once proud culture, and to show the dignity and bravery of my people.*

*My paintings depict my own uncorrupted impressions of Ojibway beliefs and legends, gods and creatures. The Department of Indian Affairs once wanted to give me art lessons, but I refused. In my opinion this would spoil me, for there is no-one who can teach me this kind of painting.*

As a result, Morrisseau's paintings are spontaneous, free and entirely original, both in their execution and as a record of Ojibway legends. The lines are simple and bold but, far from being primitive, his paintings express cultivated thought and sophisticated symbolism. Working on a stark white background in strong colours – reds and blacks usually predominate – he depicts nature and its forces. Fishes, turtles, bears, thunderbirds and people are shown with their outsides as he sees them and their insides as he imagines them. Often his characters are joined together by wavy black lines, or "lines of power", which in a compelling and unexpected way show their interrelation and interdependence.

Morrisseau's paintings combine some of the characteristics of ancient Indian rock paintings and Eskimo art. But perhaps their most startling feature is the underlying sinuosity of line so typical of oriental painting. A primordial asiatic root is common to both Indian and Eskimo cultures, according to noted Canadian folklorist Marius Barbeau, but its powerful resurgence in Morrisseau's work without his exposure to any oriental influence is in itself quite remarkable. Two semi-circles enclosed in a full circle are used by Morrisseau to represent good and evil, which are at once separate but united. The same basic symbol often occurs in oriental art.

Just as the classic battle of good and evil is symbolized in many of the Ojibway legends, the juxtaposition of opposites – good-evil, male-female, human-animal – forms the basic pattern of all Morrisseau's paintings. Also, these symbol patterns form the decorative elements of the paintings.

Morrisseau's character is also a unity of opposites. Lean and tall, he carries himself with the supreme grace and dignity of his people, while in his heart he often suffers the anguish of seeking his place in the world. He tries to reconcile his life as a free Indian nomad with the rigid behaviour demanded by his early Christian teaching. In his satchel he carries a sketch-book full of sensitive drawings of Indian gods and demi-gods, and next to it he carries his rosary. In his self-portraits he reveals all the guilt and remorse of his own excesses, and then, as if to atone for his guilt, he paints a most moving and powerful portrayal of Christ.

There is something very touching and beautiful in Morrisseau's use of rich colours and symbolism. It is a defiance of defeat and a ringing triumph of the human spirit rising above the poverty, ignorance, oppression and disease which have been his lot. Despite Morrisseau's doubts and inner conflicts, as a painter of his people and their traditions, he is sure of himself.

Success has not spoilt him, nor has his new-found wealth altered his total disregard for the value of money. He still lives at Sandy Lake Indian Reserve, one of the poorest and most isolated settlements in northern Ontario, and he is only mildly puzzled at the increasing number of admirers and film-makers who come to disrupt his solitude. But he did find it difficult to understand why the mighty transcontinental train should stop in the middle of the northern bush and wait twenty minutes to take him and his paintings to an exhibition in the east.

The white man's ways, he said simply, are truly amazing.

#  Foreword

GRANDFATHER POTAN AND THE BEAR

My Grandfather Potan lived in an Indian settlement near Beardmore in northern Ontario. He told me this story when I was a little boy.

One mild spring morning, Grandfather Potan decided to take a walk to the Beardmore garbage dump to pick up some magazines and comics thrown away by the white man. He found his white brothers rather strange and difficult to understand, and in this way he hoped to learn something about them.

As Grandfather was picking through the rubbish, he heard a truck coming, and when he looked up, he saw the Beardmore garbage truck on its way to the dump. Grandfather was ashamed to be caught taking things from the garbage by the white man, so he slipped into the bushes and hid. Eventually he found a narrow path through the forest which would take him home in a roundabout way.

*Grandfather Potan and the Bear*

He had walked about a mile and a half when he suddenly came face to face with a large brown Bear, who was busily digging at the roots of a tree at the side of the path.

The Ojibways have great respect for the Bear. According to their legends, in the distant past the Bear had a human form and was in fact an ancestor of all the Ojibways. Therefore he understands the Indian language and will never attack or fight any Indian if he is addressed properly. So Grandfather stopped and politely addressed the Bear in Ojibway:

"Oh Grandfather of all the Ojibway, please let me pass, for I am in a hurry and on my way home."

The Bear made no reply, but continued digging at the roots of the tree.

So once more Grandfather politely asked him to let him pass; still the Bear would not budge.

Grandfather was becoming very perplexed and angry, so he picked up a large stick from the ground and addressed the Bear for the third time:

"You Grandfather of us all! Go home and let me pass!"

At this, the Bear reared up on its hind legs and growled menacingly.

Now Grandfather was a proud man, and no Ojibway would tolerate such rudeness, even from an ancestor of his race.

Pale with desperation, Grandfather swore at the Bear in English:

"You ugly brute of a Bear! Go away and let me go home!"

At this, the Bear dropped to the ground and disappeared into the bushes.

Grandfather walked home deep in thought. "Things must be pretty bad with the Ojibways," he told me later, "that even our ancestor the Bear no longer understands us. Indeed, since the coming of the white man we have fallen very low, forgetting our ancient legends and ancestral beliefs.

"The time has come for us all to write and to record the story of our people; not only for ourselves but also for our white brothers so that they will be able to understand and respect us."

These were the words of my Grandfather Potan. As the years went by, I understood the truth of what he had said. So I listened to his many stories and to our legends and ancestral beliefs as they were told to me by the wise men of the Ojibway. I wrote some of them down on paper, and I drew and painted them as best I could for the Ojibway and for all the children of our white brothers to see.

NORVAL MORRISSEAU
*Beardmore, Ontario, 1968*

# Windigo

On the northern shores of Lake Nipigon there once lived an Indian trapper by the name of Windigo.

There came a particularly cruel winter, cruel both for Windigo and for all the living creatures around him. It was so cold that the air crackled and the game vanished. Windigo had to go further and further from his cabin in search of food, and he became hungrier and hungrier as he tracked wearily back each day empty-handed.

Eventually, for his mere subsistence, he was forced to drink a brew made from the bark of a tree. When even this was depleted, he was weak, hungry, cold and crazed with fear. In desperation, he prayed to an evil spirit for help.

His call was not unanswered. He had a dream, and in his dream an evil spirit promised to help him by bestowing him with supernatural powers.

When Windigo awoke from his dream, he saw that it was a clear, cold night with a full moon. He was still suffering biting pangs of hunger, but he was suddenly no longer weak or tired.

With enormous swift strides he walked south and soon approached a distant Ojibway village about a hundred miles from his home. His eyes blazed as he gave three blood-curdling yells, which so terrified all the Ojibways in the village that they fell down in a faint. No sooner had they fainted than they were all turned into beavers by Windigo's evil sorcery.

At last Windigo had enough food to eat, so he began to devour the beavers one by one. As he was eating them, he began to grow taller and taller; first as tall as a wigwam, then bigger than the trees, then taller than the highest mountains, until his head was high above the clouds. The bigger he grew, the hungrier he became. So, when he had eaten all the beavers in the village, Windigo went away in search of more food.

Meanwhile, Big Goose had been away hunting in the forest and did not know that his village had been destroyed by Windigo. As he was returning from the hunt, he was surprised not to see smoke rising from the camp-fires, and when he came nearer, he found his whole village in ruins and all its inhabitants gone.

At first he thought that a war party of some unfriendly tribe must have carried off all his friends. But when he saw the huge footprints of Windigo in the snow, he realized that something very strange had taken place. As brave as he was, he knew he could never defeat such a monstrous giant.

So Big Goose sat on the ground feeling very afraid and unhappy, and he prayed to the Great Manitou for help.

Suddenly he was startled by a noise close behind him. Then there emerged from the bushes a great Bear Medicine Man, carrying a very large medicine bag. The Bear Medicine Man put his arms around Big Goose and blew his supernatural powers into him. Immediately, Big Goose grew and grew until he became a huge and mighty giant called Missahba.

With giant strides, Missahba caught up with Windigo near Hudson Bay, and there they had a violent fight, hurling great rocks, mountains and glaciers at each other. All across the land, people trembled in their wigwams as the earth quaked around them. After two weeks Missahba killed Windigo, and the evil spell was broken.

Big Goose shrank from his giant size and became once more an ordinary Ojibway. And all the beavers devoured by Windigo were set free and again assumed their human form. The arduous journey home from Hudson Bay took them many months, but they were all very happy to reach their village once more.

## ꔹ The Forbidden Mountain

In the hilly region north of Red Lake there lived an Indian trapper by the name of Grey Beaver. Grey Beaver had three grandsons, Stone, Water and Sky, who were strong of limb and proving to be excellent hunters, but they were scornful of the old ways of the Ojibways.

On cold winter nights when the old trapper filled the little cabin with the stories and legends of their ancestors, his grandsons made fun of them, laughed contemptuously and called him a foolish old man. This was a very rude thing to do, for among the Indians it is the law that elders must be treated with great respect.

One day, Grey Beaver asked his grandsons to travel with him to Indian Lake for an important meeting. In the traditional wigwam the Medicine

*Big Goose and Bear Medicine Man*

Man was to perform the sacred rites of the Ojibways, foretell the future and give advice to those who needed it. This ceremony was known among the Ojibways as *jeesekum*, or the Shaking Tent ceremony.

Hearing this, the three brothers laughed once more. It was not for them to believe in such nonsense – they would much rather go hunting in the forest than listen to the rumblings of an old Medicine Man!

Grey Beaver travelled to Indian Lake alone. He paddled his birch-bark canoe with a heavy heart, for he had a distinct premonition that something evil was about to happen.

Meanwhile, the three brothers travelled for two days, but could not find any game. They fished, but caught nothing. They found their bad luck very strange, for usually the land around them abounded with game and the lakes and rivers teemed with fish.

On the third day, when their food was nearly finished, they approached a huge mountain rising sheer out of the forest. So high was its peak that it was enveloped in a blanket of cloud. Stone, Water and Sky knew from their grandfather's stories that this was the forbidden mountain which no Indian must climb. At its summit, according to the legend, there was a large nest which belonged to an evil Thunderbird, who did much harm to the Indians.

Needless to say, Stone, Water and Sky paid no attention to their grandfather's story. They did not believe in Thunderbirds, and although the mountain looked dark and forbidding in the leaden sky, by now they were getting very hungry, and they hoped to find some game among its numerous rocks and caves.

So they climbed for most of the day, but still they did not see any game. Dusk was falling when at last they climbed over the last few boulders and reached the peak. Weak with hunger and exhaustion, they peered over the top.

To their joy, they saw a young woman with raven-black hair and dark shining eyes sitting in front of a fire. All around her were huge rocks and tree trunks arranged in a perfect circle.

They introduced themselves and asked for food and permission to rest in front of the fire. The woman made room for them and gave them each two blue eggs to appease their hunger and some refreshing red juice to drink. So they ate their eggs and drank their juice, and when they looked up, the woman was no longer to be seen.

*Stone, Water and Sky on the Forbidden Mountain*

In her place was a huge Thunderbird, screeching fearfully, with piercing rays of light flashing from its eyes. Terrified, they could not stand to look at it, so they turned away. To their horror, they found that they themselves were slowly becoming Thunderbirds. They no longer had feet and legs: the wicked sharp claws and horny legs of the Thunderbird had replaced them.

The Thunderbird, with blinding light flashing all around it, addressed the three boys in these words:

"In three days and three nights you will become full Thunderbirds. Then we will fly together to Kukukus Lake where the Indians have a large store of tobacco, and we will destroy it."

There was a loud clap of thunder, and the Thunderbird was gone.

While this evil sorcery was taking place, Grey Beaver was sitting in front of the sacred tent at Indian Lake. In a loud and plaintive voice, he asked the Medicine Man to explain his forebodings.

There was a long silence. Then the tent began to shudder and rattle violently as all the spirits of the forest – bears, serpents and animals – and the great Water God Mishipeshu gathered in the tent to sing, talk and give their opinions.

Through his interpreter Mikkinuuk, the Turtle, the Medicine Man soon learned of the Thunderbird's sorcery, and he told Grey Beaver what had happened to his three grandsons.

Stricken with grief, Grey Beaver implored the old Medicine Man to help him. Once more there was silence inside the tent. Then it shook and rattled once more as all the creatures of the forest and the great Water God Mishipeshu gave their advice and opinions.

As the shaking subsided, the Medicine Man gave Grey Beaver three medicine arrows dipped in the sacred red onaman sand. The onaman sand had supernatural powers because, according to tradition, it was coloured scarlet by the blood of a sacred white beaver which was killed by a Thunderbird.

"Tonight, when the moon is full, you will fire these three medicine arrows in the direction of the Forbidden Mountain, and then all will be well," said the Medicine Man.

Grey Beaver did as he was told. When the moon was full, he quickly strung his bow and sent off one medicine arrow after another towards the Forbidden Mountain.

*Mikkinuuk the Turtle and the Shaking Tent*

As soon as he did so, Stone, Water and Sky experienced gripping cramps in their bellies, and were violently sick. They vomited and vomited until nothing was left of the blue eggs and the red juice given to them by the Thunderbird Woman. The ugly horny legs and sharp claws of the Thunderbird disappeared, and they were relieved and happy as their human legs and feet once more took form.

Quickly they made their escape from the nest of the Thunderbird Woman. When they reached their cabin, Grey Beaver was sitting in front of the fire, as if nothing had happened. The three brothers, feeling very ashamed of themselves, sat beside him in silence.

From that time on, they treated their grandfather and their tribal traditions with great respect, and as the years passed, they themselves earned the respect of the Ojibways.

 ## Medicine Turtle and Red Bird

Medicine Turtle was a very famous Chief and Medicine Man of the Assiniboines. One day, as he was pitching his tent not far from Eagle Nest Lake, he heard a commotion in the camp.

A party of his warriors had captured a young Ojibway brave, and they brought him before their Chief. Roughly they threw him on the ground and ordered him to pay homage to Chief Medicine Turtle. But the Ojibway refused. "When you are as strong and powerful as Red Bird, great Chief of the Ojibways," he said, "I will gladly pay you my respects. Until that time, you can torture me if you wish, but I'll pay you no homage."

This courageous talk so impressed Medicine Turtle that he ordered the Ojibway's bonds to be released, and he invited him to his tent. For many hours did Medicine Turtle listen to the exploits of Red Bird, Chief of the Ojibways.

"If these tales are true," exclaimed Medicine Turtle after the young Ojibway had finished, "then Red Bird is a far greater hero and medicine man than I. And this I cannot believe! I must challenge and defeat Red Bird of the Ojibways to show him that I am the greater chief and conjuror. Until that meeting, I'll have no peace."

And so it happened that Medicine Turtle, Chief of the Assiniboines, travelled alone in his canoe to the shores of Thunder Bay on Lake Superior to meet Red Bird of the Ojibways.

When they had met and smoked the peace pipe, Medicine Turtle explained the purpose of his visit.

"There is not room for two such great chiefs, Red Bird! One of us must be defeated. I have come here to challenge your strength, skill and medicine powers, and let the winner of our contest be the ruler of all this land!"

To this Red Bird agreed.

That evening all the Ojibways gathered around the sacred tent to watch the competition. Medicine Turtle first entered the tent, naked and with his hands tied behind his back. He then accomplished an extraordinary feat, which convinced the Ojibways that he was indeed a great conjuror possessed of a supernatural power. He made the tent shake four times in succession.

But when Red Bird's turn came, to the pride of the Ojibway braves, he performed the shaking tent ceremony no less than six times!

"You are a greater conjuror than I am," admitted Medicine Turtle, "but tomorrow I will test your strength."

The following morning they went to a dried river bed where they set six large dead tree trunks on the ground. Then Red Bird and Medicine Turtle moved several hundred yards away from the trees.

Medicine Turtle picked up a huge rock, and with all the strength he could muster, he hurled it against the trees. All but one toppled over.

"Now it is your turn, Red Bird!" he cried.

So they reset the fallen tree trunks, and Red Bird picked up a small flintstone about the size of a medicine drum. He aimed very carefully, then threw it towards the tree trunks.

As the flintstone bounced back and forth from stone to stone along the ground, sparks flew up all around it. When it struck the base of the trunks, the dry wood caught fire, and very shortly they were all burnt down to the ground.

"You have defeated me again," shouted Medicine Turtle, "but we still have to test your skill."

With these words, he pulled an arrow from his quiver and aimed it at a rock half a mile away from where they were standing. The arrow flew

19

swiftly towards the centre of the rock and penetrated halfway into the solid stone.

Seeing this, Red Bird plucked a feather from his bonnet, set it in his bow and let it fly. The feather plunged into the rock next to Medicine Turtle's arrow, and then buried itself so deeply that only an inch of it could be seen.

"You have defeated me for the third time, Red Bird!" exclaimed Medicine Turtle. "Indeed, you are a much greater and stronger man than I am."

Medicine Turtle then returned to his canoe and paddled back to Eagle Nest Lake. There he ordered the Ojibway captive to be freed and sent home.

No-one ever again challenged Red Bird, the great hero of the Ojibways, and since that time, the Assiniboines have always left the Ojibways in peace.

## Paakuk

Once upon a time, on the small island of Shanganish on Lake Superior, there lived an Ojibway fisherman with his wife Pantenata.

The fisherman had been gone for two days taking a supply of dried fish to his relatives on Spar Island. Since he was late in returning, Pantenata made the customary offering of tobacco to Mishipeshu, the great Water God, praying for his safe return.

All of a sudden, although it was still early morning, it became very dark, and a tremendous wind sprang up from the mainland. The lake boiled over and huge waves crashed down upon each other on the shores of the tiny island. In her shuddering cabin, shaken by its force, Pantenata huddled in front of a small fire and waited for the storm to pass.

Around midnight Pantenata heard weird mournful cries and a penetrating whistling noise. She was frightened by such strange sounds, but when the crying and whistling continued to fill the night, she gathered her courage and decided to investigate.

She walked through the dark in the direction of the noise, and to her horror she saw a living creature, half human, half skeleton, with long flowing hair and coal black eyes set in sunken cheeks. This awful creature was stuck in a narrow crevice between two rocks.

*Medicine Turtle and Red Bird*

Seeing Pantenata, the strange creature whimpered pathetically, and continued its eerie whistling. Then in an ancient Ojibway tongue which Pantenata could hardly understand, it begged her for help.

"If you will free me from this crevice, I will grant you one wish," croaked the strange creature. "My name is Paakuk. Hundreds of years ago I committed an evil crime, and as punishment I must fly around and around the world, between the moon and the sun, day in and day out, till the world's end, when I shall be judged by all men.

This is Paakuk's story :

A long time ago I lived with my younger brother, Wabese, in a small settlement near Favourable Lake. Not far from our settlement was the mighty lodge of Black Bear Medicine Man, who had a daughter named Silver Birch.

No matter how I tried to win her favour, Silver Birch loved only my brother. So I became jealous and began to hate him, although I tried to conceal my feelings.

One day when Wabese was away hunting, I went to the cave of an evil conjuror. I gave him all my tobacco, my best buckskin dress and rings of copper, and in exchange he gave me a little bag made of hide containing some yellow powder. This he advised me to put in Wabese's drink.

When Wabese returned from the hunt, I slipped the yellow powder into his drink, and it dissolved immediately. Unaware of my evil intentions, he drank it all, for he was very thirsty. To my delight, he began to shrink, and he grew smaller and smaller until he was the size of a corn-cob. Then his arms and legs disappeared and he turned into a piece of yellow limestone.

I seized him and put him in the small deerskin bag, then travelled as fast as I could to Sandy Lake, where I threw him into the clear water. The lake bubbled up, and the stone which was once my brother dissolved rapidly, colouring the water limestone grey – as it remains to this day.

Then I hastened back to Favourable Lake, for now there was no obstacle to prevent me from taking Silver Birch as my wife.

On the way back, I was struck by the stillness of the forest through which I was travelling. There was no wind, not even a gentle breeze, and all the creatures of the forest had vanished. I could hear no insects buzzing and no birds singing. The sky, which had been bright a few minutes before, darkened and became as black as midnight; and yet I could see no stars and no moon. I felt that I was the only living creature in an alien world.

Paakuk

And as I travelled in this complete silence, a sudden fear gripped me by the throat. I had used evil powers to do harm. I had offended the Indian law which states that no-one should use sorcery without a just cause, or the spirits will turn against him. The nearer I got to home, the more afraid I became of the vengeance of the spirits.

On my way I passed the medicine tent of the Black Bear. There were about five hundred Indians seated in a huge semi-circle around it. They sat in stony silence and no-one greeted me as I paddled by. I was sure I heard the roar of Mishipeshu, the great Water God, and the devil Windigo arguing loudly in the tent. I was very much afraid of their accusations. So as not to hear them, I bound my ears with a buckskin blanket and paddled swiftly past the Shaking Tent to my cabin. I was very tired from my journey and soon went to sleep.

In my sleep I saw a great serpent with huge teeth blowing hard at my cabin until it disintegrated. Then the serpent lifted me in its great teeth and flew with me high up into the sky. Sometimes when we passed near the sun I was unbearably hot, but when we passed near the moon I was numb to the bone with the cold.

"When I awoke from me dream," continued Paakuk, "I was flying around and around the earth, between the moon and the sun. I have been flying like this for hundreds of years and I must continue to fly aimlessly till the end of time to pay for the evil which I have done."

Pantenata was moved by Paakuk's story. She felt sorry for him, for he looked so wasted and miserable.

"Grant me one wish: Let my husband come home soon," cried Pantenata against the high wind, "and I'll set you free!" Paakuk gave a whistle of assent.

Pantenata then grabbed him by the heels and prised him loose from the crevice in the rock. Paakuk gave a piercing yell, and with a tremendous whistle he shot up into the sky and was soon gone from sight.

Pantenata made her way to her cabin, wondering if her wish would be granted. She was astonished when suddenly the wind dropped and the lake became as smooth as glass.

And there in the cabin, sitting near the fire, was her husband, waiting for her.

# The Magic Mushrooms

Long ago, two Indian brothers named Swift Current and Silver Cloud lived in a village near Lake Nipigon. One bitter year, the winter was long, hard and cold, and game was very scarce. At last, when there was very little food left in the village, Swift Current and Silver Cloud went hunting. At the end of a luckless day, a deer darted across their path, and although they wounded it badly, it managed to run into the woods. Afraid of losing sight of it, they chased it through the forest.

The chase was hard and arduous over a frozen wintery course abounding in large rocks and fallen tree trunks, all half buried in deep snow.

In one last frantic leap over a large boulder, the deer vanished from sight. Gasping with exertion, Swift Current and Silver Cloud climbed over the big rock, and although the terrain all around it was quite flat and open, the deer was nowhere to be seen.

Swift Current and Silver Cloud were puzzled by this unexpected disappearance. Their village was very short of food, and they desperately hoped to kill some game soon. However, they were nearly exhausted, so they decided to rest and partake of the little food they still had with them.

Swift Current was searching for wood to start a fire when suddenly he heard a shout from his brother. So he ran to see what had happened.

Silver Cloud was standing on a rocky ledge and seemed to be peering intently at the smooth surface of the stone. As Swift Current came up to the rock, he was amazed to see a gaping hole in it, which led like a tunnel into a large green field, dotted with small shrubs swaying gently in the wind and warmed by a sunny sky. And there, scattered over the field, were clumps of succulent red mushrooms with bees and multi-coloured insects buzzing around them.

As he peered into the tunnel, Swift Current was very much afraid. By some strange chance, they must have stumbled upon a magic field in a supernatural world. He thought it would be wise to leave this enchanted place at once before something sinister happened to them.

He voiced his fears to his brother, but Silver Cloud only laughed. "We are cold and hungry," he said. "It is the will of Great Manitou that we should make ourselves warm under the sunny sky and eat the succulent mushrooms to appease our hunger."

With these words, he climbed down the hole and ran into the field. Swift Current was sure there was a spell upon the field, but before he could utter another warning, Silver Cloud picked a bunch of mushrooms and ate them.

A feeling of calm and peace descended upon him. He was no longer cold and hungry, and he called to his brother to join him in the comfort of the sunny field. Little did he realize that by the magic of the supernatural he himself was becoming a bright red mushroom under the mysterious sky.

Swift Current watched in horror as the spell overtook his brother. Quickly he took note of the exact spot in the green field where his brother stood, and he ran for help.

He had been running through the forest for hours, when suddenly in the narrow path he stumbled into a large form. It was the Bear Medicine Man who was gathering some bark from the trees.

Weak with exhaustion, Swift Current sank to his knees and implored the Bear Medicine Man for help. The Medicine Man gave him some food, and after listening to his story, handed him a medicine bag made of deer hide and a magic arrow.

"You will fill this medicine bag with the sacred onaman sand, which you will find at Onaman Lake," said the Medicine Man. "With this magic arrow you will kill an eagle; then you will pluck three feathers, one from each wing and one from the tail, and attach them to the medicine bag. As long as you carry the sacred onaman medicine bag you will be safe to enter the world of the supernatural.

"You must then pick the mushroom and bring it out of the enchanted world. Plant it in the snow, and sprinkle the sacred onaman sand on it."

Swift Current did as he was told. After travelling for many days he reached Onaman Lake, where he filled the deer-hide bag with the sacred onaman sand. Then he fired the magic arrow in the direction of the eagle's nest. Soon he heard a great cry in the sky, and a huge golden eagle tumbled down to the ground. Swift Current quickly plucked the three feathers and attached them to the medicine bag.

He raced back to Mystery Lake, where he found the big rock with its hole leading into the enchanted field. Although he was still very much

*Swift Current and Silver Cloud, and the Magic Mushrooms*

afraid, he entered the narrow tunnel and, clutching his medicine bag, he ran into the field.

He remembered exactly the spot where his brother had turned into a mushroom. He picked the mushroom, and ran back through the hole in the rock to the outside world. There he planted the mushroom firmly in the snow and spread some of the sacred onaman sand over it. The spell of the supernatural was broken, and Silver Cloud assumed his human form once again.

The two brothers were overjoyed at being together again, and started for home. The medicine bag of the Bear Medicine Man brought them even greater luck, for on the way they killed a large deer and saved their village from famine.

That is why, even to this day, the Ojibways are afraid to eat mushrooms.

## Ishka-Maatuk and the Thunderbird Boy

Once upon a time along the shores of Kashishibog Lake there was a large settlement of Ojibways. Their Chief was a powerful Medicine Man, and he had a beautiful daughter named Ishka-Maatuk.

Ishka-Maatuk was very much alone, for her mother had died when she was very young, and she had no brothers or sisters. The Medicine Man was very jealous of his only daughter, and all the young men of the village were afraid of his powers.

One day a visitor appeared on the shores of Kashishibog Lake. This was the Limping Bear, a sorcerer of some repute, who came from the little Grand Rapids on the Barren River. Several weeks before, he had dreamed of Ishka-Maatuk, whom he had never seen. In his dream he was so much impressed by her beauty that he decided to take her as his wife.

So he travelled for many days to Kashishibog Village. He recognized Ishka-Maatuk immediately from his dream, and finding her even more beautiful than he had hoped, he wanted her more than ever.

At first the old Indian Chief would not give his consent to the Limping Bear. The scorcerer tried to induce him with numerous gifts, and finally tricked him into smoking some tobacco mixed with grey mushroom powder

Bear Medicine Man

– a very potent and evil medicine when properly prepared. Soon an oblivious sense of well-being clouded his judgment, and he gave the Limping Bear his daughter's hand.

Ishka-Maatuk was surprised and dismayed at this turn of events. She did not want the Limping Bear as a husband. He was cross-eyed, he limped badly and he had a violent temper. Not wanting to embarrass her father, she stole away in the middle of the night and paddled westward.

She travelled in her canoe for many weeks and many months, passing swift rivers and crossing lakes and portages until she reached a clear, deep, blue lake encircled by huge snow-capped mountains. Ishka-Maatuk pulled her canoe to the shore of the lake, ate some berries and went to sleep, for she was very tired.

She was awakened from her sleep by a loud clap of thunder and a flash of lightning. At first she could not understand what had wakened her, for the sky was blue and clear and no clouds were to be seen. But violent thunder and lightning continued briefly, the suddenly the storm ceased. And there, standing right in front of her, was a tall young Indian with the most brilliant and penetrating eyes she had ever seen.

Ishka-Maatuk was very startled at his sudden appearance, and she asked him who he was.

"I am the Thunderbird Man in the form of an Indian," he replied, "and I have come to take you as my wife."

He then took her by the hand. Out of nowhere there was a crash of thunder and lightning continued briefly, then suddenly the storm ceased. where the Thunderbird Man kept his wigwam and his medicine lodge.

For several years Ishka-Maatuk lived happily as wife of the Thunderbird Man, and soon they had a son named Paisk.

But as the years went by, Ishka-Maatuk began to miss her native land and the people she used to know. So she asked her husband for permission to take Paisk to visit them. He agreed, and led them to a cloud. There was a brilliant flash and a loud rumbling, and they found themselves at the bottom of the mountain.

Tied to a rock on the shore of the clear blue lake was the canoe in which Ishka-Maatuk made her journey so many years ago. As they were making ready to leave, the Thunderbird Man warned Paisk never to point his arm at any living thing. "If you do, you will become a Thunderbird forever."

For many months Ishka-Maatuk and Paisk travelled eastwards, until

*Ishka-Maatuk and Paisk, the Thunderbird Boy*

Ishka-Maatuk saw the familiar shores of Kashishibog Lake, lined with the wigwams of her people. She was welcomed by her friends. The Old Chief was very glad to see his daughter again, and was proud of his grandson Paisk.

He still felt ashamed for being so badly tricked by the Limping Bear so many years before. He told his daughter that he took his revenge by casting a powerful spell on the Limping Bear's canoe. It turned to a stone just as he was nearing his village and sank at the bottom of little Grand Rapids with the evil sorcerer in it.

Young Paisk was very happy at his mother's village. He played with the other Indian children and he learned how to hunt and fish. He was very much respected by his friends.

One day, Paisk and three of his friends were picking berries in the bush when suddenly an enormous elk leapt from behind a tree and stormed past the startled boy.

"Look!" shouted Paisk to his companions, pointing his arm at the running elk. He had no sooner pointed than, with a deafening thunderclap, a bolt of lightning shot from his arm, instantly killing the great elk. Terrified, his three friends ran back to the village, leaving a very perplexed Paisk in the bush.

As soon as the village elders heard of what had happened, they realized that Paisk was no ordinary Indian boy, but that he possessed some evil power. They were afraid that he might destroy them all, so they decided to banish Ishka-Maatuk and Paisk from the village forever.

The next day, the old Indian Chief returned from hunting to find his daughter and grandson gone. He immediately demanded an explanation. When told of the strange events of the day before, he thought silently for a while, and then he addressed the elders in these words:

"My brave and trusted friends, you have committed a grave error in sending Paisk away from the village. It is obvious to all of us that he possessed the secret of thunder. Had he stayed with us, our enemies would have been afraid of us and the Ojibways would be the rulers of the earth. Let us make haste and bring them back to the village."

Upon hearing these words, the strongest paddlers in the swiftest canoes set out in pursuit of Paisk and Ishka-Maatuk. They travelled for several days until on the fifth day they spotted the canoe of Ishka-Maatuk tied to a tree at Eagle Rock Lake. A small fire was burning on the side of a rock and the voices of Ishka-Maatuk and Paisk could plainly be heard over the water. So they called to them.

Suddenly, out of the clear blue sky there was a tremendous crash of thunder, and when they ran to the rock for cover, Ishka-Maatuk and Paisk were no longer there.

High in the sky, they heard the loud, piercing cries of Thunderbirds. When they looked up, they saw three Thunderbirds with wild flashing eyes flying westward.

Very much afraid, the Indians returned to their village. That was the last they heard of Ishka-Maatuk and Paisk, the Thunderbird Boy.

## Wee-sa-kee-Jack (Whisky-Jack)

Hundreds of years ago there lived among the Ojibways a powerful Medicine Man and Chieftain whose name was Whisky-Jack.

Whisky-Jack had three wolves as his blood brothers. They were his constant companions and took good care of him. When it was very cold, the wolves covered him with their bodies; when it was hot, they fanned him with their tails.

Whisky-Jack had great strength and cunning, and many Indians were indebted to him for saving them from sorcery and peril. One year there had been a great flood, and Whisky-Jack rescued all the living creatures around him by herding them onto a large raft which he made of stone. He was very proud of his powers, and as time went by, he became more and more arrogant and obnoxious.

One day Whisky-Jack stood on the shores of Lake Superior throwing large rocks into the water and uttering defiance to all the creatures of the lake. By chance, one of the rocks hit Mishipeshu, the Water God, right on the nose.

Mishipeshu was furious at Whisky-Jack's lack of respect, and he put a curse on him.

From the bottom of Lake Superior there sprang a monstrous trout, Misee-na-way-guis, which snatched Whisky-Jack from the shore and swallowed him in one quick gulp.

Imprisoned in the dark cave of the monster's stomach, Whisky-Jack was suddenly powerless, and it was too late for him to regret his brash behaviour. His prison was wet and slippery, he was unaccustomed to the dark and very unsteady on his feet. Also, he was very seasick, as the giant trout heaved from side to side on its very erratic course of travel.

Soon, however, Whisky-Jack got used to the darkness and began to plan his escape.

Misee-na-way-guis had snatched him so quickly from the shore that he had left his bow and arrows behind; but his knife was still tied to his belt. He sliced a small opening through the monster's stomach, and saw that its bones towered at least twenty feet above him. Working laboriously with his knife, he managed to cut loose one of these giant fishbones. He seized it with both hands and thrust it with all his might through the monster's heart.

The enormous trout thrashed violently in the water, then floated dead to the surface of the lake. Whisky-Jack climbed up the monster's throat, hoping to escape through its mouth, but even after his careful plotting and meticulous labour, he found its jaws snapped shut and the way barred by its large teeth.

Whisky-Jack suddenly realized that all his strength and cunning were of no avail, and that he would soon perish if he were not rescued. So he prayed to Great Manitou for help.

Manitou listened to his plea, and saw that his punishment had humbled him. So he sent a flock of ravens to prey upon the dead monster. They descended on the floating trout and started picking at its flesh.

Soon nothing was left of the giant trout but it skeleton, and at last Whisky-Jack was free from his prison. He prised loose one of its huge teeth, and using it as a paddle, he paddled the great skeleton across Lake Superior to his home.

Whisky-Jack finally realized that even if he was a mighty Chieftain and Medicine Man, he was wrong to be so proud and arrogant. So to show his humility to the Indians around him, he often assumed the form of an ordinary jack rabbit. For now he knew that in the eyes of Great Manitou all living creatures, large or small, proud or humble, are equal; and that a great chief is no better than a lowly rabbit.

Whisky-Jack

# The Silver Curse

Once upon a time, not long after the first white man was seen in North America, a white fur trader named Balthazar settled among the Assiniboines on the shores of Deception Lake, not far from today's Manitoba-Ontario border.

Balthazar cruelly cheated and exploited the friendly Indians. He was rapacious and greedy, and he demanded more and more precious beaver pelts in exchange for his coloured beads and worthless trinkets. Like all the white men of the time, he wanted to make a quick fortune in the new world and then return to live in comfort among his white brothers in Europe.

One day a young Assiniboine brave returned to his tribe on the shores of Deception Lake. He had been a captive of the Ojibways for many months, but after numerous adventures he finally escaped and found his way home. During his captivity he learned many of the customs and secret rites of the Ojibways, for the Indians usually treated their captives well, eventually allowing them to marry and to become full members of the tribe.

On his return to the village, the young brave was welcomed joyfully by his family and his tribe. A big potlach and dance were held in his honour, and for this celebration he dressed in all his best skins and adorned himself with some beautiful metal ornaments given to him by the Ojibways. It was not long before these ornaments attracted the attention of the rapacious Balthazar, who was quick to recognize them as pure silver. He demanded to know at once where the young brave had obtained them, for he knew that if he could but trace the source of the silver, he would be rich in no time, and could leave this savage land for the comforts and civilization of Europe.

The young Assiniboine told him that the ornaments were given to him by the Ojibways who lived on the shores of Thunder Bay on Lake Superior. Although he had lived with them for many months and learned much about them, they would not tell him where they obtained their silver. It would be unlucky for a stranger to know, they said.

Undaunted, Balthazar left the Assiniboines with a greed in his heart and his hopes high at the prospect of a quick fortune. After two weeks of travel

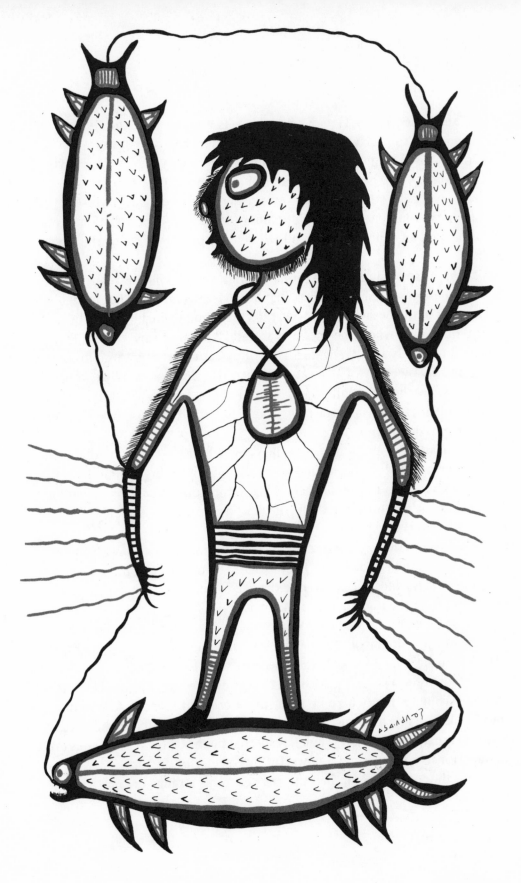

*Maymaygwasiwuk, Interpreter of Dreams*

he reached the shores of Thunder Bay. He was welcomed by the Ojibways, who made him comfortable and gave him food and a large wigwam.

But try as he might, he could not learn where they found their silver. Months went by and he was losing hope of ever learning their secret.

Then he had a stroke of luck. By accident, he overheard two squaws talking outside his tent. They were planning to take large birch-bark baskets with them on an expedition the following night to a place called the Silver Island.

Balthazar spent a restless night in his wigwam, making his plans. In the morning he announced to his hosts that he was going hunting. But in fact he hid himself in the bushes just outside the village and waited for nightfall.

At midnight, when the moon was full, Balthazar saw two Ojibway canoes slip silently into the water. The canny fur trader crept into his own canoe and followed them at a safe distance. The Indians paddled steadily until they reached a small island several miles from shore. Here they beached their canoes, and carrying their large birch-bark baskets, they stepped onto the shore.

Balthazar had seen enough. Now he knew where the Ojibways obtained their silver, and he became excited at the thought of having it himself.

It took ten days to paddle back to the Assiniboine village at Deception Lake. There he commandeered one of their largest canoes and two of their strongest paddlers.

With visions of riches before his eyes, Balthazar drove the two paddlers to the limit of their endurance. They reached Thunder Bay on the evening of the fifth day, and as they were exhausted from their arduous journey, they settled for the night and were soon asleep.

The same night the Medicine Man of the Ojibways had a strange dream. First he saw a white moon and a white star, and then he saw the Water God Mishipeshu fighting a wicked water serpent with three heads.

As soon as he awoke, the Medicine Man hastened to a large rock on the shore of Thunder Bay where he made an offering of tobacco to Maymay-gwasiwuk, a hairy and mischievous water spirit living under the earth's crust. Maymaygwasiwuk was much respected by the Ojibways as a creature of superior intelligence and a powerful interpreter of dreams.

Soon the Medicine Man had the answer to his strange dream. A white

*Balthazar and the Sleeping Giant*

moon and a white star – a white stranger was coming. Mishipeshu fighting an evil three-headed serpent . . .

"The white man was not alone – there were three strangers coming with some evil intent," Maymaygwasiwuk instructed the Medicine Man.

Balthazar's disappearance so soon after the Indians' visit to Silver Island could mean only one thing – he had discovered their secret.

So the Medicine Man prayed to the great God Manitou. Manitou heard his plea, and he immediately sent a huge giant to Thunder Bay to protect the Ojibways. The giant lay down upon the little island, hiding it from sight, and promptly went to sleep.

The next morning, Balthazar and his companions woke up and paddled across Thunder Bay in the direction of Silver Island. On and on they went, but Silver Island was nowhere to be seen. The white trader was angry and bewildered when they reached the exact spot where he had seen Silver Island. All they could find was a small rock sticking out of the water. One of the Indians struck it with his paddle as they passed it by. Little did he realize that this was the big toe of the sleeping giant.

The giant, so rudely disturbed from his slumber, gave a great grunt and rolled over in the water. Huge waves were caused by this movement, which rolled across Thunder Bay and flooded its shores. Balthazar's canoe upset, and he and his two companions floundered and drowned.

To this day, the Ojibways consider silver very unlucky and will have nothing to do with it. And to this day, the giant lies asleep on Silver Island. You can see him from Port Arthur on a clear day when you look across Thunder Bay.